HAL LEONARD
STUDENT
PIANO
LIBRARY

Indigo Bay

By Jennifer Linn

Showcase Solos

HAL•LEONARD®
CORPORATION
7777 W. BLUEMOUND RD. P.O. BOX 13819 MILWAUKEE, WI 53213

Indigo Bay

Jennifer Linn

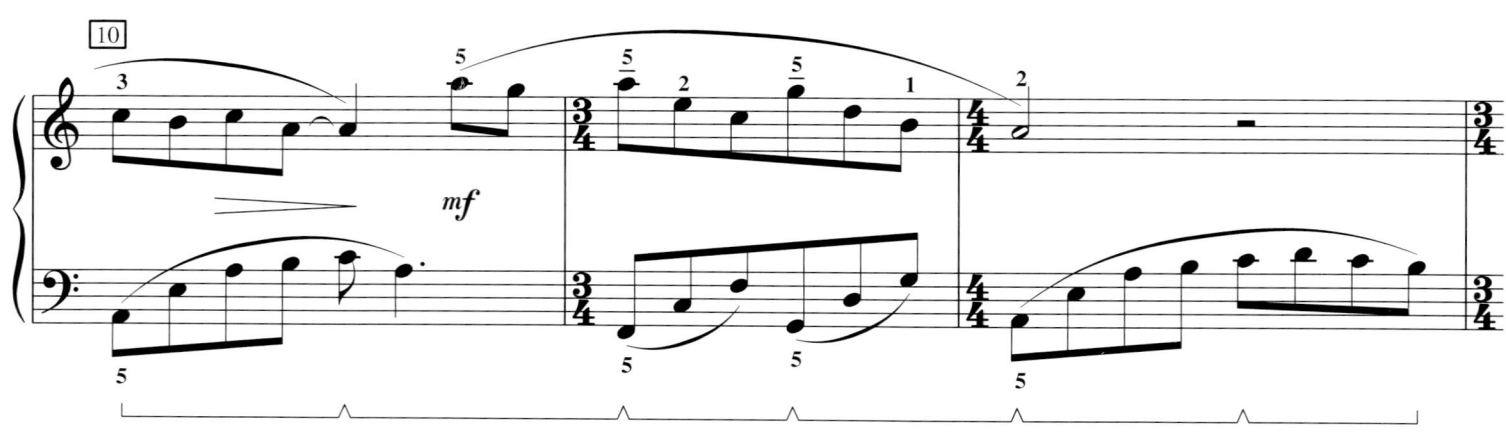

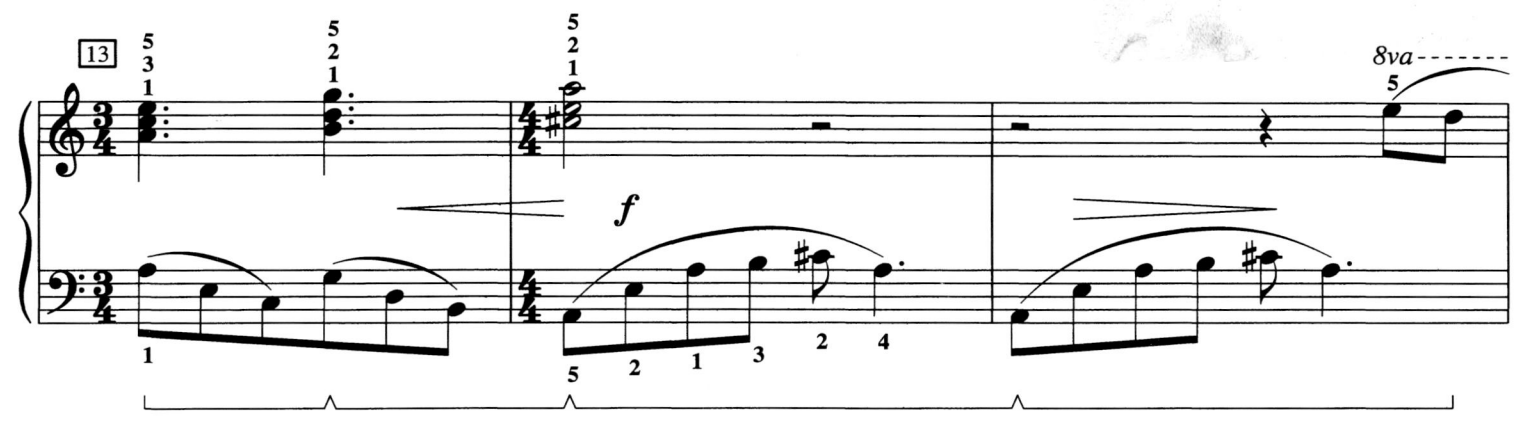

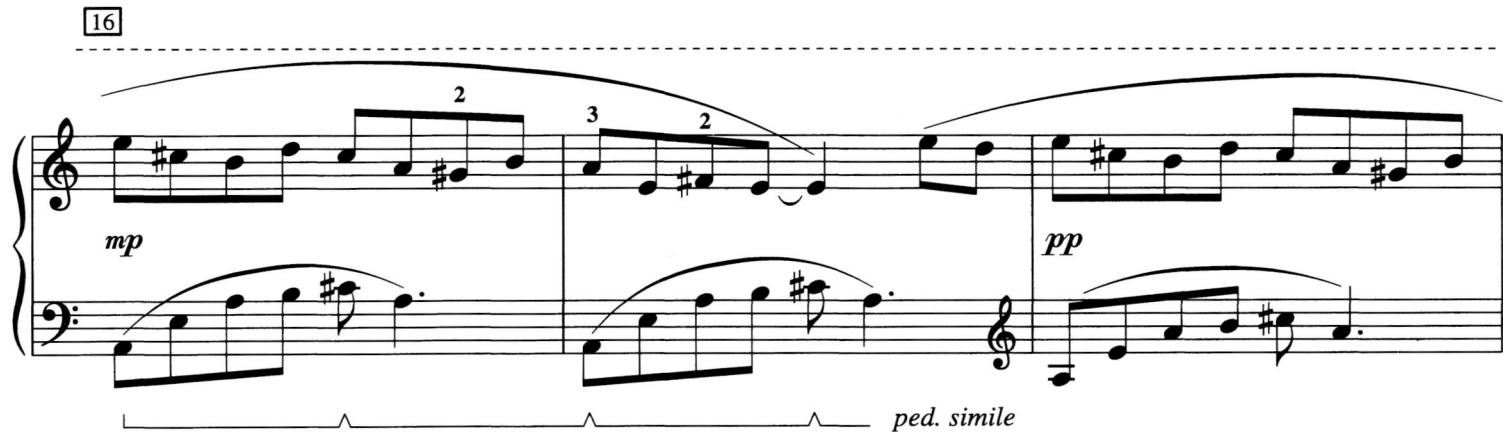

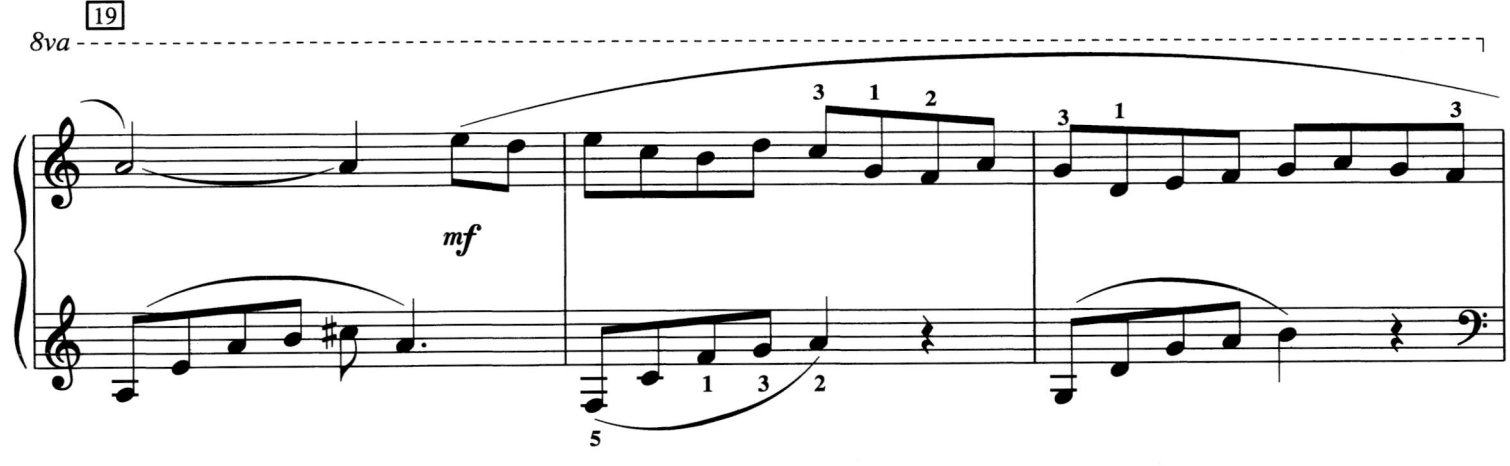

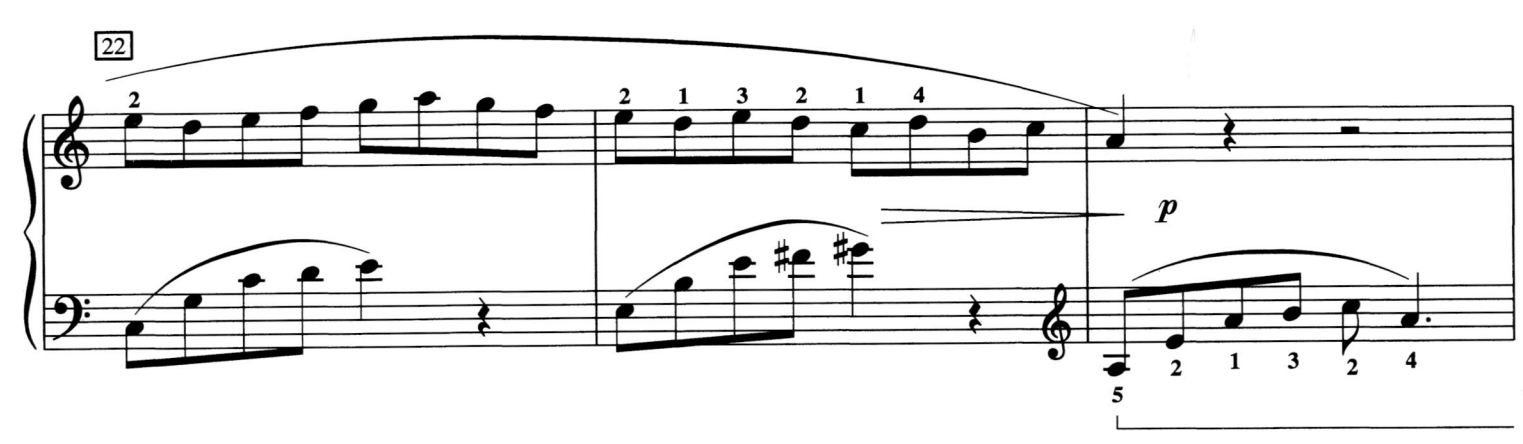

4

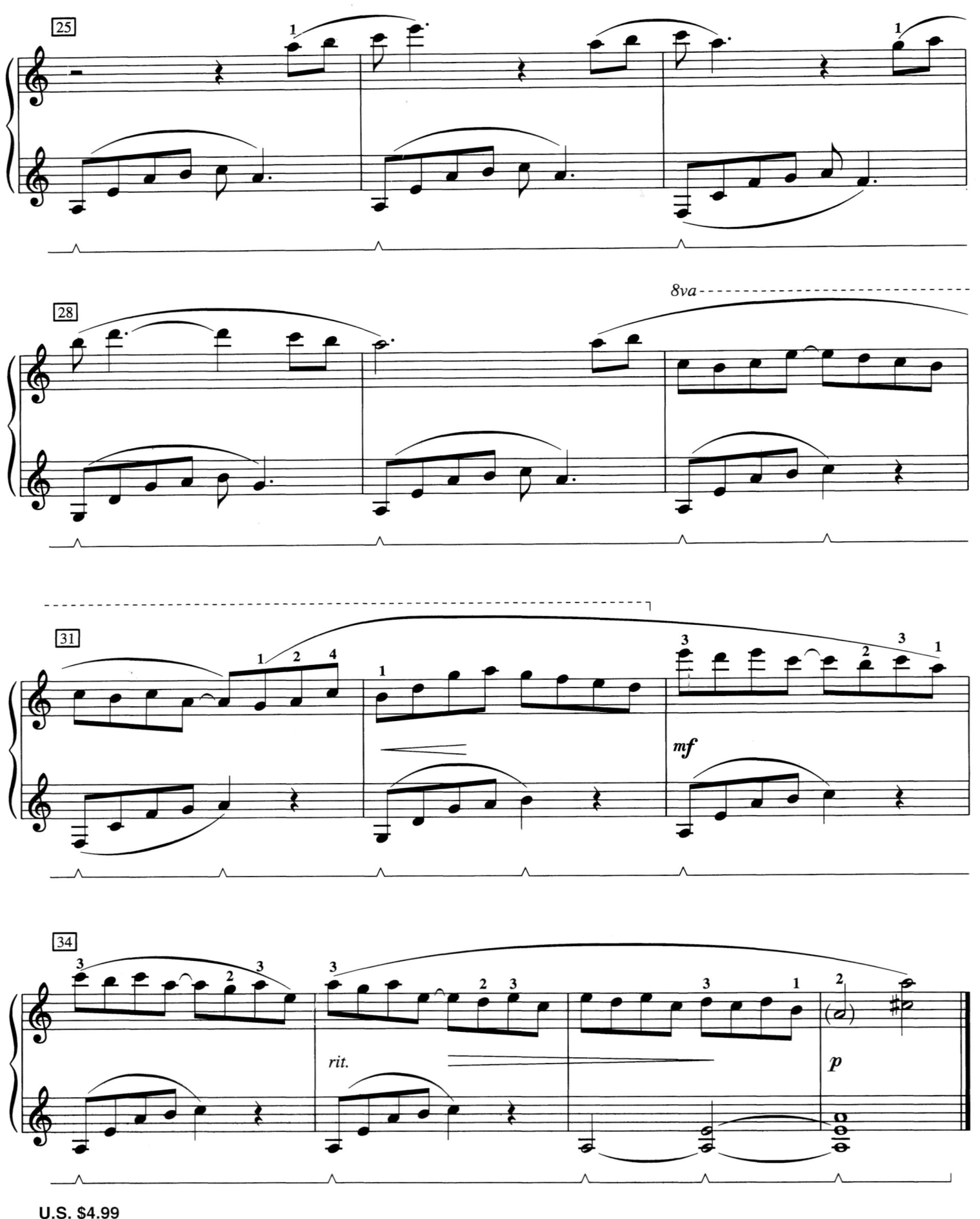

0 73999 96144 7

HL00296144